LOUIS

Night Salad

by metaphrog

The publisher acknowledges support
from Creative Scotland towards
the publication of this title

Graphic novel

ISBN 978-0-9545984-1-9

www.metaphrog.com

For David Chalmers

LOUIS
Night Salad
by metaphrog

It started with an accident...

PERHAPS IT WAS THE CHEMICAL SPILLAGE? OR JUST THE FALL: A NASTY BUMP... LOUIS WASN'T EVEN SURE WHAT TO TELL HIS AUNT.

OF COURSE, HE WASN'T A BIRD DOCTOR. AN EXPERT. MOSTLY HE WORKED WITH FRUIT.

NOW IT WAS ADVICE HE NEEDED. ABOUT A SICK BIRD.

AND HIS AUNT OFTEN GAVE ADVICE.

WHATEVER THE CAUSE, FC IS NOW UNWELL.

DING DONG

I HOPE AUNT ALISON CAN HELP US.

IT HAD BEEN THE MIDDLE OF A PINEAPPLE SITUATION.

A TRICKY OPERATION.

LOUIS COULD NOT EVEN COUNT THE NUMBER OF TIMES HE'D BEEN BACK OVER IT ALL IN HIS HEAD.

I SHOULD HAVE BEEN MORE CAREFUL.

INITIALLY, HE HAD FELT A DREADFUL LURCH, AN AWFUL PANIC RUSH THROUGH HIS BODY.

NOW, HE WASN'T SURE HOW HE FELT.

LOST. OR, AT LEAST, A LITTLE LOST.

AND NERVOUS, AND ANXIOUS.

OF COURSE, IT WASN'T REALLY POSSIBLE TO GET LOST IN A HOUSE YOU KNEW.

LIKE OPENING A CUPBOARD TO FIND AN UNEXPECTED STAIRCASE.

LIKE WEARING THE BIG GLOVES FOR THE FIRST TIME.

OH MY! I DON'T REMEMBER PUTTING MY BOWL AWAY.

BUT IT WASN'T THAT KIND OF LOST FEELING.

A DIFFICULT SENSATION TO PINPOINT.

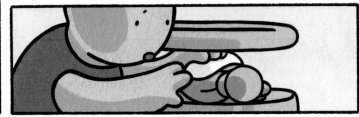

WAS THAT THE SECOND OR FIRST BELL?

IF INDEED IT WAS THE SECOND BELL THEN, LOUIS KNEW IT WAS TIME TO START WORK.

HE'D BEEN TOO LOST IN HIS THOUGHTS.

EARLIER THERE HAD BEEN THE POSTMAN.

... AND LOUIS WAS GLAD HE'D MANAGED TO FINISH HIS LETTER ON TIME.

12

WRITING TO HIS AUNT HAD SEEMED SENSIBLE. AT FIRST IT ALMOST MADE HIM FEEL BETTER.

HE HAD DECIDED NOT TO ASK THE POSTMAN FOR ADVICE.

NOW LOUIS WISHED HE COULD SPEAK TO SOMEONE.

VISITORS WERE A RARITY.
TWO IN ONE WEEK WAS DOUBLY UNUSUAL.

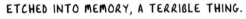

ALTHOUGH, LOUIS WASN'T SURE IF THE ARRIVAL OF THE HEFTY NEW CHEMICAL CONTAINERS COUNTED AS A VISIT.

SINISTER SPECTRAL SHAPES. LOOMING IN THE FOG OF A MORNING, THERE IN THEIR GARDEN.

ETCHED INTO MEMORY, A TERRIBLE THING.

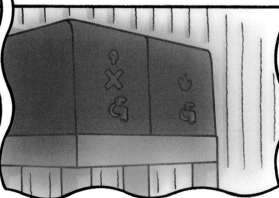

14

MEMORIES DISSOLVED IN TEARS...

I'M SORRY.

LOUIS WISHED HE COULD SPEAK TO THE KINDLY WOMAN.

HE COULDN'T SAY FOR CERTAIN, BUT SHE LOOKED LIKE SHE MIGHT KNOW ABOUT BIRDS.

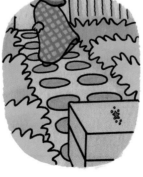

IT WASN'T POSSIBLE TO MAKE VISITORS JUST APPEAR.

THE BOX HADN'T ARRIVED BY THE USUAL POSTAL MEANS.

A MYSTERY. A SPECIAL DELIVERY.

LOUIS DIDN'T KNOW WHO THE WOMAN WAS OR EVEN HOW TO CONTACT HER.

ANYWAY, IT WAS IMPOSSIBLE TO TELL IF SOMEONE WAS KNOWLEDGEABLE AT A GLANCE.

PINEAPPLES HAD BEEN LOUIS' AREA LATELY.

I WOULDN'T LIKE TO SAY I'M AN EXPERT.

THE THOUGHT OF WORK MADE HIS ANXIETY GROW.

NOT WHILE FC IS ILL...

PERHAPS READING TO HIS FRIEND WOULD HELP...

Adrift on the ocean, Dreams washing over their craft, Louis and FL sailed together towards the moon

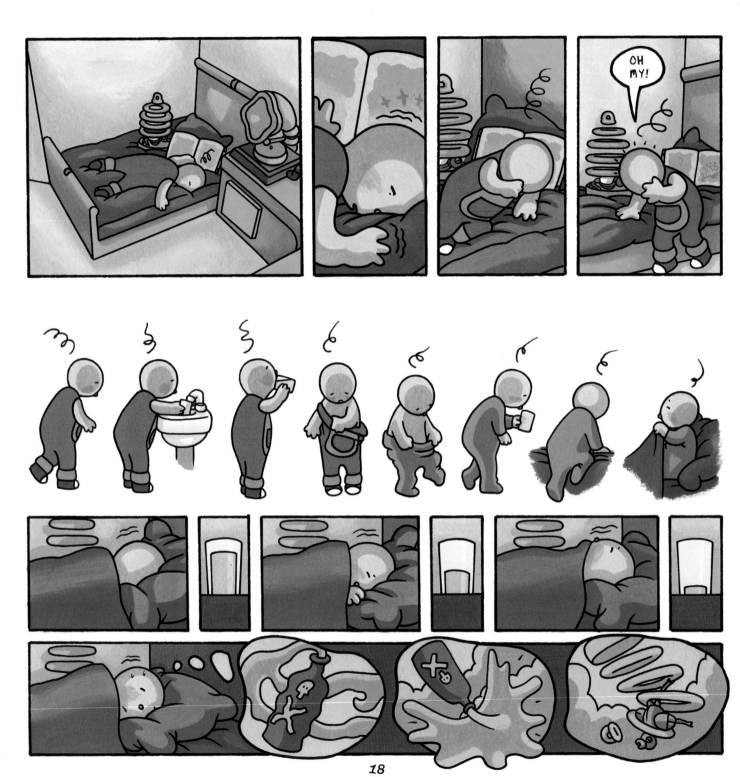

THE
NIGHTMARE
ENDED
LOUIS'
SLEEP.

HE
AWOKE
HOPING
IT HAD ALL
JUST BEEN
A TERRIBLE
DREAM.

NOT ONLY WAS
HIS FRIEND
UNWELL, NOW
HE WAS
HEARING
THINGS.

A
SLEEPLESS
NIGHT
WOULDN'T
HELP.
THE AIR
SEEMED
TO
CLOSE
IN
OPPRESSIVELY.

THERE
IT
WAS
AGAIN.

A NOISE

REPEATING.

WAS
THE
SOUND
OUTSIDE
OR
WAS
IT
EMANATING
FROM
INSIDE
HIM?

HE NEEDED
AIR.

LIGHT.

LOUIS HADN'T EXPECTED LIGHT.

HIS SLEEPING HAD SUGGESTED NIGHT.

OH MY!

RECENTLY LOUIS HAD LOST TRACK OF TIME PASSING...

BUT NOW HE KNEW THINGS WERE NOT RIGHT.

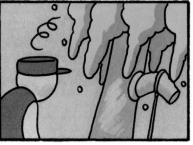

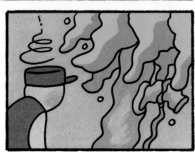

CONTINUING MIGHT RESULT IN A SECOND SPILLAGE. THE LAST THING THEY NEEDED!

WORKING INSTEAD ON FRUIT FOR HIS SECOND SHIFT SEEMED SENSIBLE. PRACTICAL.

IN FACT, IT WAS ENTIRELY POSSIBLE HE HADN'T NOTICED THE CHANGE OVER BELL.

PUMPING PRESENTED PROBLEMS.

UNPREDICTABLY.

POP

ADVICE WOULD BE DISPENSED FOR A CREDIT. BUT THE ADVICE DIDN'T ALWAYS MAKE SENSE.

Pay Money
Say Words

I DON'T KNOW WHEN MY AUNT WILL REPLY...

THE MAIN PROBLEM WAS FORMULATING THE CORRECT QUESTION.

COMFORTER

PLEASE ASK A QUESTION.

"MY FRIEND IS NOT WELL AND... I FEEL TOO SICK TO WORK... I DON'T KNOW WHAT...?"

Pay money say words

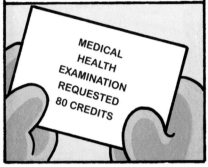

THERE IT WAS. THE COMFORTER HAD BEEN UNFORTHCOMING BEFORE ON THE SUBJECT OF BIRDS.

MEDICAL HEALTH EXAMINATION REQUESTED 80 CREDITS

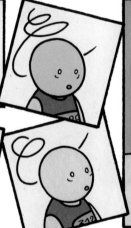

LOUIS HAD NEVER BEEN ON A BOAT BEFORE, BUT HE IMAGINED THIS WAS WHAT IT WAS LIKE TO FEEL SEASICK.

READING WITH FC HE HAD DREAMED HE WAS SAILING SEVERAL TIMES, BUT IT HADN'T MADE HIM FEEL AT ALL SEASICK.

NOT THIS TERRIBLE SENSATION. HE WOULD HAVE NOTICED.

...

SO... HIS LITTLE FRIEND IS UNWELL...

SHINY!

HE DOESN'T FEEL HE CAN "CONCENTRATE, WITH FC LIKE THIS".

A SECOND READING REVEALS THE ANGUISH BETWEEN THE LINES.

LOUIS KNOWS HE'S NOT A BIRD DOCTOR.

BUD DOCTOR?

HMM... YES. AN EXPERT.

HE FEELS HE KNOWS "A LITTLE ABOUT FRUIT. BUT FC IS A BIRD".

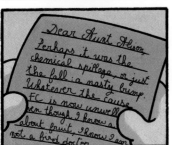

Dear Aunt Alison,
Perhaps it was the chemical spillage, or just the fall: a nasty bump. Whatever the cause FC is now unwell even though I know a lot about fruit, I know I am not a bird doctor.

AUNT ALISON'S TO OFFER ADVICE.

HMMM... SOMETHING UNIMAGINABLE. EVEN, IMPOSSIBLE. ...

THE FRUIT OF THE RAINING TREE!

A MYTH YOU SEE. A FALSITY.

?

BUT HE'S GOOD WITH FRUIT.

EVEN THOUGH I LOATHE TO SAY SO.

... AND THIS WILL SET HIM PUZZLING. UNDERMINE HIM...

I THINK THAT CALLS FOR A TUNE!

For some reason, the doorbell had seemed unusually loud.

Even with his sensitive hearing system Louis was used to the morning ding dongs.

Of course, he couldn't expect a reply from his aunt Alison. Not immediately.

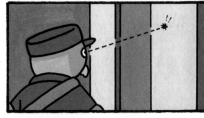

Letters were unusual. And, recently, after moving house, her correspondence had ceased for some considerable time.

Louis could understand that.

HE HE!

HE HE HE!

louis artapoint 3120 Hamlet

I SHOULD HAVE MENTIONED YOU'VE NEVER BEEN ILL BEFORE.

IT HAD SEEMED OBVIOUS. LOUIS HADN'T PUT HIS WORRIES INTO WORDS.

DINC DONC

GOOD EVENING!

DR OZAENA.

MEDICAL HEALTH EXAMINATION REQUESTED. 80 CREDITS.

SAY AHH!

AHHH!

NOT YOU!

TAKE TWO BLUE PILLS EVERY THREE HOURS BEFORE BREAKFAST.

THREE RED PILLS BEFORE FOOD.

YOU MAY EXPERIENCE QUEASINESS ...

MEANS THE MEDICINE IS WORKING.

SIMPLY SIGN THE DOTTED LINE.

31

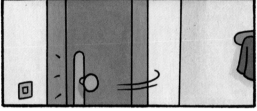

LOUIS HADN'T REALISED THE MEDICAL HEALTH EXAMINATION WOULD BE SO CONFUSING. HE HADN'T EVEN HAD A CHANCE TO ASK ABOUT FC!

HE HADN'T IMAGINED IT THEN. AUNT ALISON HAD REPLIED.

My dear Louis,
I'm so sorry to hear about FC's sudden illness.
The only cure I ever heard of for a sick bird is the
fruit of the raining tree. It is to be
administered before 18 bells from
becoming unwell. I do hope your
little friend gets better. It would
be such a shame to have to turn
him over to pet disposal.
signed: Your loving
Aunt

HE HAD NEEDED ADVICE AND, WELL, HERE IT WAS.

THE FRUIT OF THE RAINING TREE.

LOUIS COULDN'T EVEN IMAGINE WHAT THE SEEDS WOULD LOOK LIKE. HE CERTAINLY WASN'T AN EXPERT ON RAINING TREES!

AND HE DIDN'T LIKE THE SOUND OF PET DISPOSAL ONE LITTLE BIT!

HOW MANY BELLS HAD THERE ALREADY BEEN?

KEEP YOUR EYES ON THE INVISIBLE PRIZE!

THE INVISIBLE PRIZE!

HAMLET'S NUMBER ONE GAME SHOW!

YOU COULD BE A LUCKY WINNER! JUST KEEP YOUR EYES...

...ON THE INVISIBLE PRIZE! RIGHT AFTER THIS BREAK!

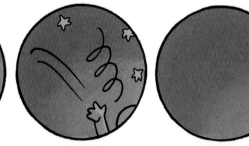

THERE WAS NO DOUBT: HE'D LOST TRACK OF TIME!

AND NOW HE HAD THE AWFUL FEELING IT WAS RUNNING OUT!

HE HE HE!

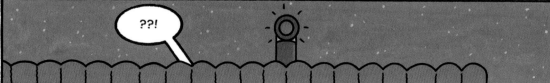

??!

HE DIDN'T NEED HIS SENSITIVE HEARING SYSTEM TO REGISTER THE DULL THUMP THAT CAME FROM BEHIND HIM.

PERHAPS ONE OF THE HEFTY NEW CHEMICAL CONTAINERS HAD BECOME DISLODGED? FALLEN TO THE GROUND, LIKE LOUIS HIMSELF. STUCK. UNABLE TO GET UP.

FC MIGHT THINK HE'D LEFT HIM ALL ALONE...

TO BE DISPOSED OF...

THREE SMALL LEAVES DRIFTED SKYWARD BEFORE RETURNING WITH GRAVITY ON THEIR JOURNEYS DOWN.

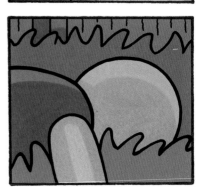

THE DEPTH OF SILENCE WAS SUFFOCATING.

FROM FAR ABOVE HIS HEAD DRIFTED A DISTANT CHUCKING SOUND.

MORE OF A PHUT, ON CLOSER HEARING.

UNPLEAS-ANTLY LOUIS COULD NOT CRANE HIS NECK TO SEE.

GRADUALLY THE SOUND GREW CLOSER AND LOUIS COULD SEE A TINY LIGHT, HIGH IN THE SKY.

LOUIS HAD NEVER SEEN A LIGHT THERE BEFORE. PERHAPS IT WAS A STAR?

AS HE PONDERED, THE LIGHT SEEMED TO MOVE.

IT'S A SHOOTING STAR FC!

EXPLORERS OFTEN USED STARS FOR NAVIGATION. IT WAS UNLIKELY, HOWEVER, THAT THEY WOULD USE A SHOOTING STAR.

NEEDING A FIXED POINT.

OR POINTS.

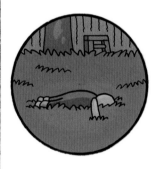

RUMINATING ON THESE THOUGHTS TRANSPORTED LOUIS INTO A STRANGE REALM, CLOSE TO THE SURFACE OF A DREAM.

THAT NIGHT, HIS BED FELT ODDLY MOSSY.

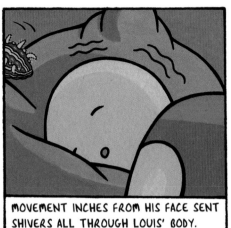

MOVEMENT INCHES FROM HIS FACE SENT SHIVERS ALL THROUGH LOUIS' BODY.

ANXIOUS FIGURES HURRIED PAST.

TOWARDS A SHADOWY NARROWING PATH.

FEAR DEFORMED FACES, MADE FOOTING UNSURE.

YOU SHOULD HURRY YOU KNOW!

WOULDN'T WANT TO END UP AS A SNACK!

A SNACK!

CATERPILLAR LIKE THAT: POISONOUS GREEN FEATHERS. BEAUTIFUL BUT CRUEL. PARALYSIS YOU SEE.

THEN SNACKS AT LEISURE.

SEEN IT HAPPEN WITH MY OWN EYES!

CARNIVOROUS CATERPILLARS PROBE BELOW THE SURFACE, GET VERY CURIOUS, VERY HUNGRY.

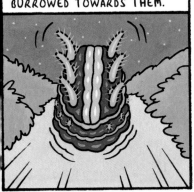

AS THE SMALL FIGURE EXPLAINED, THE CATERPILLAR BURROWED TOWARDS THEM.

THE SUDDEN REALISATION BROUGHT HORROR.

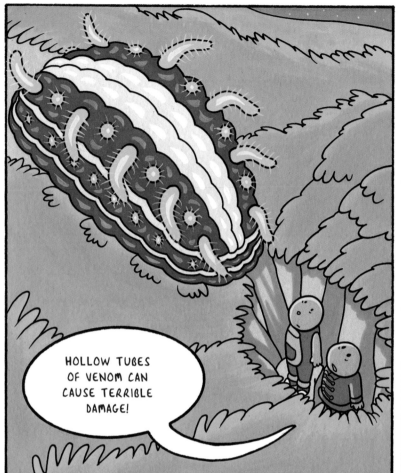

HOLLOW TUBES OF VENOM CAN CAUSE TERRIBLE DAMAGE!

PARALYSIS.

LOUIS SAID THE WORD OUT LOUD WITHOUT MEANING TO.

YES, PARALYSIS. AND A NASTY RASH.

AS WITH CHEESE AND OTHER POROUS MATERIAL, MANY HOLES ARE PARTIAL, BLOCKED. NOT TUNNELS. UNTUNNELS IF YOU LIKE.

LOUIS DID LIKE THAT.

UNTUNNELS.

HE SAID THE WORD WITH RELISH.

IT ISN'T REALLY A WORD, BUT THERE'S ALREADY AN "UN" IN TUNNEL YOU SEE.

LOUIS COULD SEE THAT.

DO YOU LIKE WORDS?

VERY HANDY FOR PUTTING THINGS ACROSS.

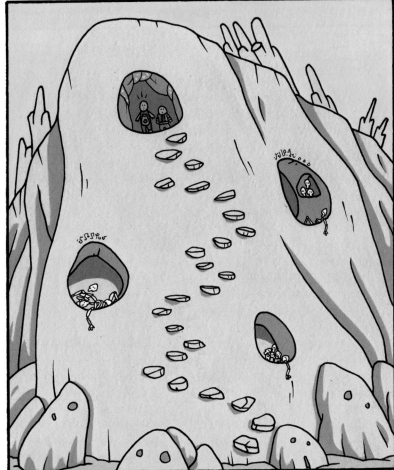

TINY DWELLINGS NESTLED BENEATH LOOMING SANDSTONE CLIFFS.

AND BEYOND THE CLIFFS A SUDDEN DESERT: GIGANTIC FIGURES FORMING IN THE SWIRLS OF SAND.

DISENCHANTED DJINN THEIR SMILES LIKE THE WIND.

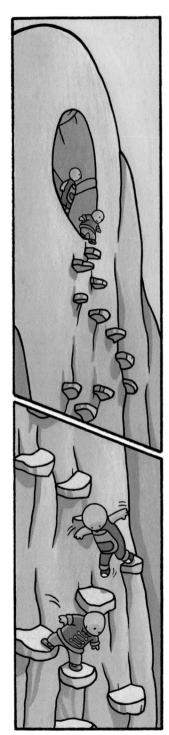

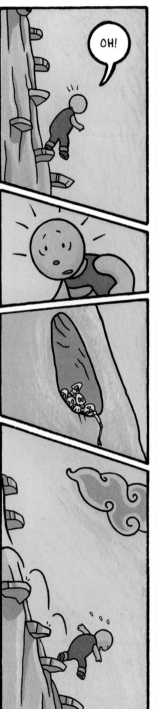

SOME NEVER EVEN GET PAST THE CLIFFS YOU SEE...

LEFT ON THE LEDGE, MADNESS FOLLOWS SUN-STROKE, THEN FOLLOWS ...

OH MY!

VERY EASY TO TAKE A WRONG TURNING IN A PANIC: QUICK DECISION, LONG REGRET ...

FIRST THEY LOSE THEIR WAY AND THEN THEY LOSE THEIR MINDS.

BAKING UNDER THE RELENTLESS SUN.

NOT EVERYONE IS CHASED BY CATERPILLARS OF COURSE !

MANY ARE LURED BY THE TREASURE OF THE CAVES.

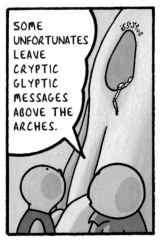

SOME UNFORTUNATES LEAVE CRYPTIC GLYPTIC MESSAGES ABOVE THE ARCHES.

TREASURE!?

WELL, THAT'S WHAT THEY SAY BUT...

PERSONALLY...

I DOUBT IT. WITH A SILENT B.

LOUIS REALISED HOW SELFISH HE HAD BEEN. HIS LITTLE FRIEND WAS UNWELL, AND HE HADN'T EVEN GIVEN THE MATTER A THOUGHT.

BUT THAT WAS IMPOSSIBLE!

FC'S SILENCE HAD BEEN A WORRY, URGENT, PRESSING... HAD WEIGHED HEAVILY ON HIM...

I WANTED TO ASK YOU ABOUT FC.

MY FRIEND: HE'S A BIRD.

A BIRD!?

HE HASN'T REALLY BEEN HIMSELF.

LOUIS HAD SAID FC WASN'T REALLY FEELING HIMSELF. BUT THE TRUTH WAS...

HE DIDN'T KNOW IF A BIRD COULD BE BROKEN.

BUT THAT WAS WHAT IT LOOKED LIKE!

IT DIDN'T BEAR THINKING ABOUT.

IS YOUR BIRD SICK?

DOES IT EAT CATERPILLARS?

CAN YOU MAKE IT EAT CATERPILLARS?

THOUGHT CREASED THE SMALL FACIAL FEATURES MOMENTARILY.

ONLY CURE I EVER HEARD OF FOR A SICK BIRD WOULD BE THE FRUIT OF THE RAINING TREE.

A RAINING TREE?

RAIN!!

RAIN!! RAIN!! RAINING!!

SCHOKKADAY!! SCHOKKADAY!! SCHOKKADAY!! MOOTTANTTA!!

BECAUSE THE BULK OF THE CITY LIES UNDERGROUND, THIS UPPER LEVEL ACTS AS A DISTRACTION.

A DISTRACTION?

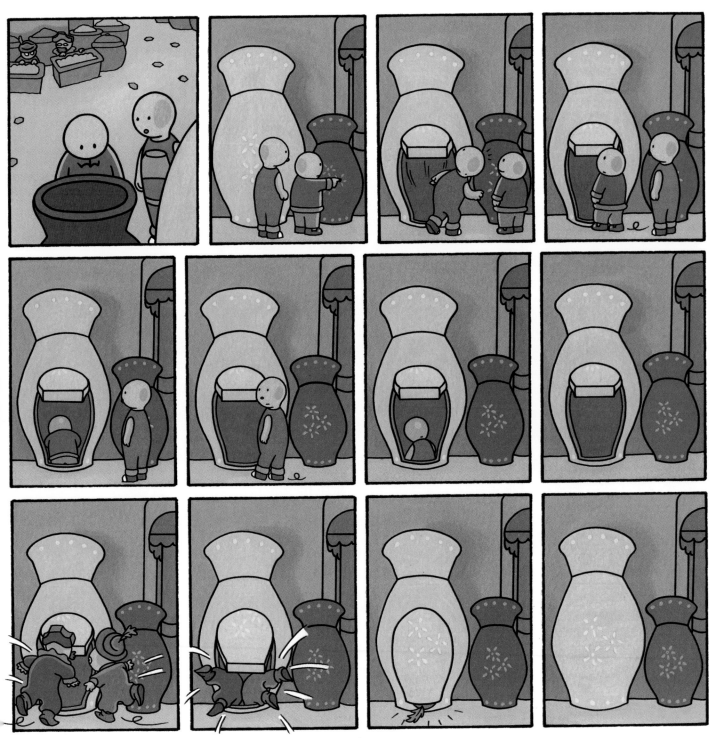

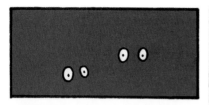

SUNLIGHT SEEMED TO SPARKLE ON A MILLION MINARETS.

WITHOUT A BORROWER'S CARD THE LIBRARY WON'T HELP US.

WE CAN PICK MINE UP AT MY HOUSE: IT'S ON OUR WAY.

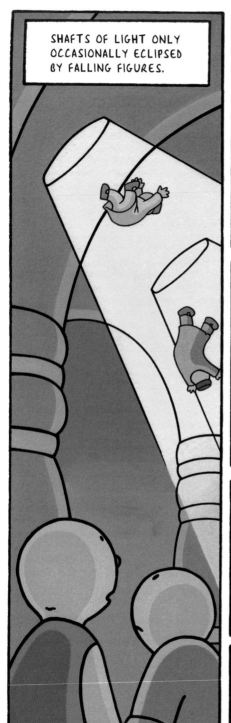

SHAFTS OF LIGHT ONLY OCCASIONALLY ECLIPSED BY FALLING FIGURES.

LIGHT IS USED TO PRODUCE HEAT AND OTHER ENERGIES FOR THE INNER WORKINGS OF THE CITY ITSELF.

ABOVE LIES THE DESERT OF HIDDEN WORLS.

THIS IS THE WORL OF RESIDUAL DOUBT.

UNDER THE SHIFTING SANDS THE DESERT TRANSFORMS. TRAVELLERS TUMBLE. PLUMMET... NEVER TO BE SEEN AGAIN....

YES: PLUMMET IS THE WORD...

... NEVER KNOW WHEN YOU'RE GOING TO GO, INTO THE SWIRLING SANDS BELOW.

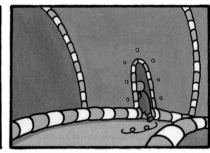
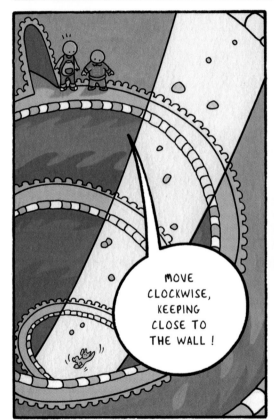

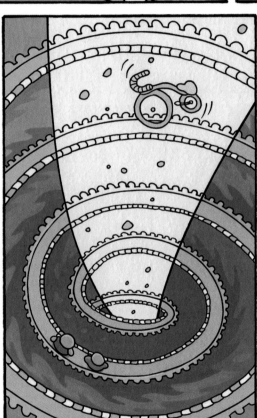

THIS IS MY HOUSE. WE NEED MY TICKET, AND PROBABLY WATER. JOURNEY HIGH AND DRY.

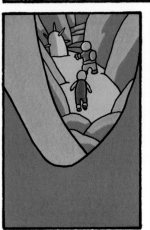

SO, ARE OUR FRIENDS ANY CLOSER TO THEIR GRAIL?

GRAIL?

THE TREASURE...

THEY CAN'T JUST HAVE VANISHED! THEY'RE ON A ROCK!

SO THEY VANISHED! POSSIBLY DISAPPEARED THROUGH THE TOP OF THE WORL?

VANISHED!

OR INVENTED AN INVISIBILITY OINTMENT AND WOAH....

SLIP!

OUCH!

PLAF!

OOPH

IT BIT ME ON THE AHHH...

...

A FALSE PRICK...

INGENIOUS ....

?

56

MAZES HAVE BEEN CONSTRUCTED TO ENSNARE THE UNWARY...

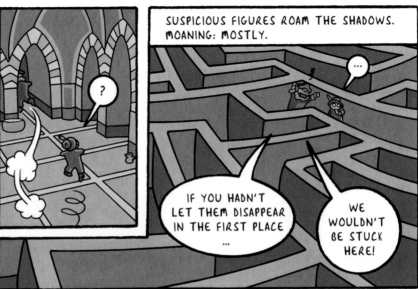

?

SUSPICIOUS FIGURES ROAM THE SHADOWS. MOANING: MOSTLY.

...

IF YOU HADN'T LET THEM DISAPPEAR IN THE FIRST PLACE ...

WE WOULDN'T BE STUCK HERE!

DEPARTMENT ?

IS THERE A DEPARTMENT FOR SICK BIRDS ?

...

BIRDS WOULD BE ORNITHOLOGY: DISEASES PATHOLOGY... HMMM... LET ME SEE... WELL: VETERINARY PATHOLOGY OR ORNITHOLOGY. BOTH ARE IN CHAMBER FIVE OF HALL FIVE. THAT'S ON LEVEL FIVE.

SECOND ARCHWAY ON YOUR LEFT.

THANK YOU.

EXCUSE ME...

WE'RE SEEKING THE CURE FOR A SICK BIRD.

IT'S FOR MY FRIEND. FC. FORMULAIC COMPANION.

LOUIS WASN'T SURE WHY HE'D GIVEN FC'S FULL NAME. PERHAPS THE SERIOUSNESS OF THE SITUATION.

MY AUNT WROTE TO ME: SHE SUGGESTED THE FRUIT OF THE RAINING TREE.

DID I HEAR SICK BIRD?

IT COULD BE CAGE LAYER FATIGUE.

HIS AUNT MENTIONED THE RAINING TREE.

A CURE!

A CURE?

WELL ...

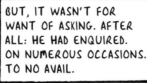

"YOUR AUNT OBVIOUSLY KNOWS HER BIRDS."

"IS SHE AN ORNITHOLOGIST?"

"A KEEN HOBBYIST?"

MOMENTARILY LOUIS FELT A FLUSH OF EMBARRASSMENT AT JUST HOW LITTLE HE KNEW ABOUT HIS AUNT.

BUT, IT WASN'T FOR WANT OF ASKING. AFTER ALL: HE HAD ENQUIRED. ON NUMEROUS OCCASIONS. TO NO AVAIL.

"AN AVICULTURALIST?"

"I DON'T THINK SHE'S AN EXPERT."

"HMMM."

"NEED LOCAL KNOWLEDGE ..."

"STOP TREADING ON MY BEARD!"

"WHY DON'T YOU JUST GIVE IT A GOOD TUG!?"

"ER...HUM... ONLY CURE I EVER HEARD OF FOR A SICK BIRD IS THE FRUIT OF THE RAINING TREE..."

"... ADMINISTERED, ORALLY, EIGHTEEN BELLS FROM BECOMING UNWELL."

"MOST LIKELY REGION FOR YOUR RAINING TREE WOULD BE ..."

Here Be Monsters

Cave of R Yo

Irregular Isthmus

"HERE."

"ACROSS THE IRREGULAR ISTHMUS..."

Here Be Monsters

Cave of R Yo

Irregular Isthmus

"IF YOU'D LIKE A COPY OF THE MAP I CAN SKETCH IT. MATTER OF MAYBE MINUTES ..."

"THANK YOU."

PREDATORS LURK BEHIND BOULDERS, UNDER ROCKS, HIGH ON LEDGES AND EVEN IN (SPECIALLY ADAPTED) HOLLOWS BENEATH THE SAND SURFACE.

BEST TO REST BEFORE WE SET OFF IN THE MORNING.

BY NIGHT THE DESERT IS TRULY TREACHEROUS.

SPECIALLY ADAPTED?

IN BRACKETS: IS ADDITIONAL INFORMATION.

MY FATHER BUILT IT WHEN I WAS LITTLE.

SPENT DAYS POLISHING THE LENSES, WORKING OUT A SYSTEM...

MAGNIFICATION.

WE COULD STUDY THE STARS.

OCCASIONALLY, THE MOON APPEARS AS IF ON A JOURNEY.

FOR FRUIT, IT IS HARD TO SAY. WE'LL NEED A LITTLE LUCK.

THE LIBRARIANS SAID THIS SEEMS THE MOST LIKELY REGION.

Fruit
?
valley

ACCESS ACROSS THE DESERT PLAINS ... LARGELY DEPENDS ON WORLS.

Cave

THEN TRAVERSING THE IRREGULAR ISTHMUS... THAT'S THERE.

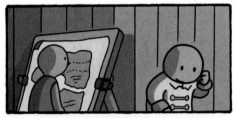

OLIVES, CAPERS AND CACTI BUTTONS, PICKLED NOPALES, MARINATED MUSHROOMS ...

... TOMATOES (DRIED IN THE SUN), OLIVE OIL, UNLEAVENED BREAD.

IF YOU'D LIKE: SOME SEEDS, TUNAS AND PITAYAS (CAREFULLY PEELED TO REMOVE GLOCHIDS), AND DATES.

MUNCH MUNCH

GULP GULP

IF YOU'VE EATEN ENOUGH ... ?

WE SHOULD SLEEP, GATHER STRENGTH FOR TOMORROW.

GOOD NIGHT!

GOOD NIGHT!

 ZZZZZZZ

OF COURSE, GETTING A GOOD NIGHT'S REST WAS ESSENTIAL. LOUIS KNEW JUST HOW IMPORTANT IT WAS.

 ZZZZZZZ

BUT SOMEHOW HE COULDN'T SLEEP AND HIS MIND SEEMED TO RACE.

NO PARTICULAR THOUGHT COULD EVEN BE CAUGHT AND HELD IN PLACE, IT WAS JUST A RACE.

BENEATH HIM THE SLEEPING MAT WAS PERFECTLY COMFORTABLE. AND, THERE WAS NO DOUBT HE WAS TIRED.

STILL HIS THOUGHTS RACED. ROUND IN THOUGHT CIRCLES. SPIRALS.

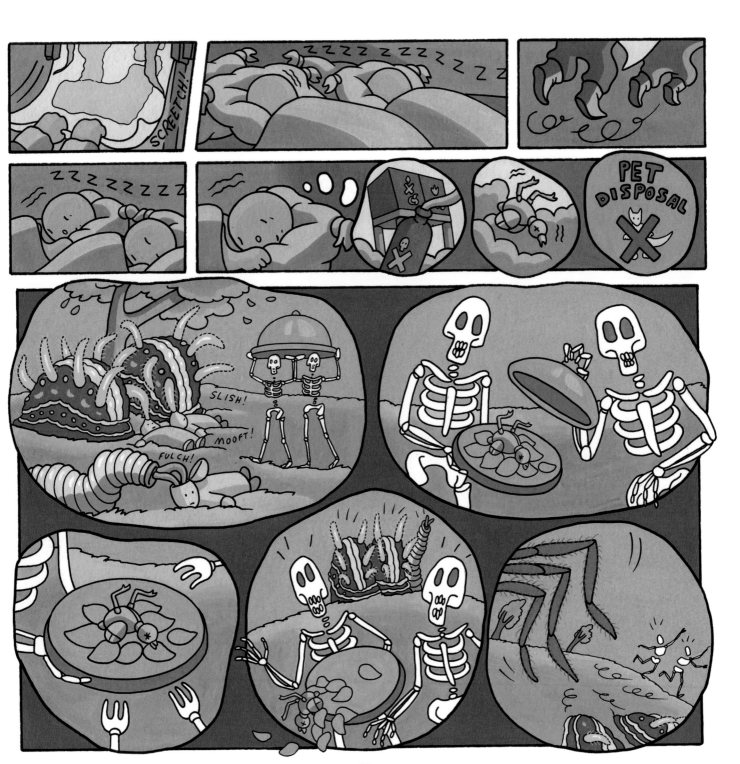

OH MY!

I...

...THOUGHT I HEARD SOME-THING.

?

NOCTURNAL NIBBLING?

INTRUDERS?

CREAKS IN A STRANGE HOUSE THROUGH THE NIGHT.

?

?
?

WHO WOULD WANT TO... IT DOESN'T MAKE SENSE.

...AND IN SUCH A HURRY.

...

ANYWAY IT'S ALL IN HERE ... I MEMORISED IT.

WE SHOULD PACK QUICKLY AND SET OFF BEFORE THE SUN IS HIGH...

WHO WOULD EVEN KNOW IT WAS HERE?!

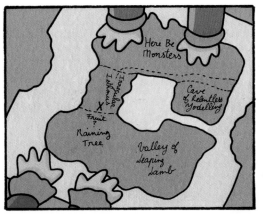

DO THEY EXPECT ME TO BELIEVE THEY'RE IN PURSUIT OF FRUIT!?

FRUIT?

PHROOT PROOT !!?

THIS RAINING TREE.

I MEAN, THIS IS THE DESERT!

DESERTS ARE DRY! THERE IS NO RAIN.

ONLY A VAST EXPANSE OF...

WELL...

... SAND MOSTLY.

THE RAINING TREE.

IT MUST BE SOME NONSENSICAL CODE FOR TREASURE!

PATHETIC.

HOWEVER...

WISE TO KEEP AN EYE ON OUR LITTLE FRIENDS.

TREE MAY BE CODE BUT THE MAP MAY BE PHONEY.

YOU SEE!

LEFT OUT A LITTLE TOO EASILY YOU SEE. FOR YOU AND ME.

COULD BE A SNEAKY LITTLE TRICK TRAIL TO THROW US OFF THE SCENT.

O BUT I CAN SNIFF SUBTERFUGE.

TRIED TO LEAD US A MERRY LITTLE DANCE.

A MERRY LITTLE PRANCE.

EVEN THE MOST EXPERIENCED TRAVELLER COULD FIND THEMSELVES IN UNEXPECTED PREDICAMENTS.

LOST IN THE SHIFTING SAND, A LONELY TRAVELLER TENDS TO THIRST.

LOUIS COULD FEEL HIMSELF GETTING HOTTER.

WE SHOULD STOP FOR A WHILE. SHELTER FROM THE MIDDAY SUN.

GLUP GLUP

GLUP GLUP

CACTUS JUICE. MOST REFRESHING.

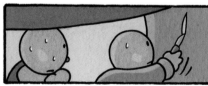

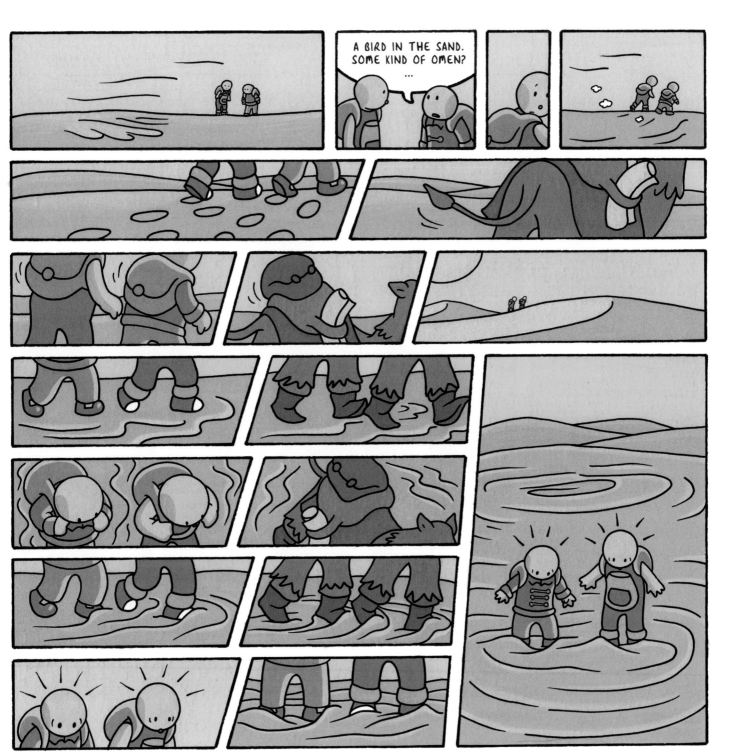

NIGHT WAS FALLING. THEY REACHED THE EDGE OF THE DESERT PLAIN.

CATERPILLARS CROSS THESE ROCKS LIKE MIGRATING MOSS.

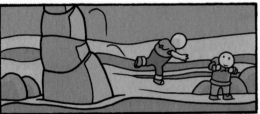

THE RAINING TREE IS AN IRREGULAR TREE...

THESE TREES ARE ODDLY PODDY.

BEYOND THE DESERT, HIGHER TEMPERATURES HAD FORMED GLASS.

DEAD RIVER BEDS...

THEIR CONSTELLATIONS...

THE NIGHT'S LUMINOUS MUSHROOMS.

IT'S BEEN A LONG DAY.
SOME REST WILL
BE MOST HELPFUL.

IF MY CALCULATIONS ARE CORRECT,
WE SHOULD SOON REACH
THE RAINING TREE.

THE RAINING TREE.
LOUIS' HEART SWELLED
IN ANTICIPATION.

IF ONLY THE FRUIT
REALLY COULD
HELP FC.

IF MY CALCULATIONS ARE CORRECT, WE SHOULD SOON REACH THE RAINING TREE.

LOUIS HADN'T EVEN MEMORISED THE MAP. THE LIKELY AREAS.

THREE TINY CLOUDS DRIFTED ACROSS THE NIGHT SKY.

OF COURSE, LOUIS WASN'T AS FAMILIAR WITH THE SKY AS HIS FRIEND HAD BEEN.

AN ASTRONOMER, AN EXPERT, WOULD HAVE NOTICED IT AT ONCE.

BUT, THE LONGER HE LOOKED, THE MORE CERTAIN HE BECAME ...

A NEW STAR.

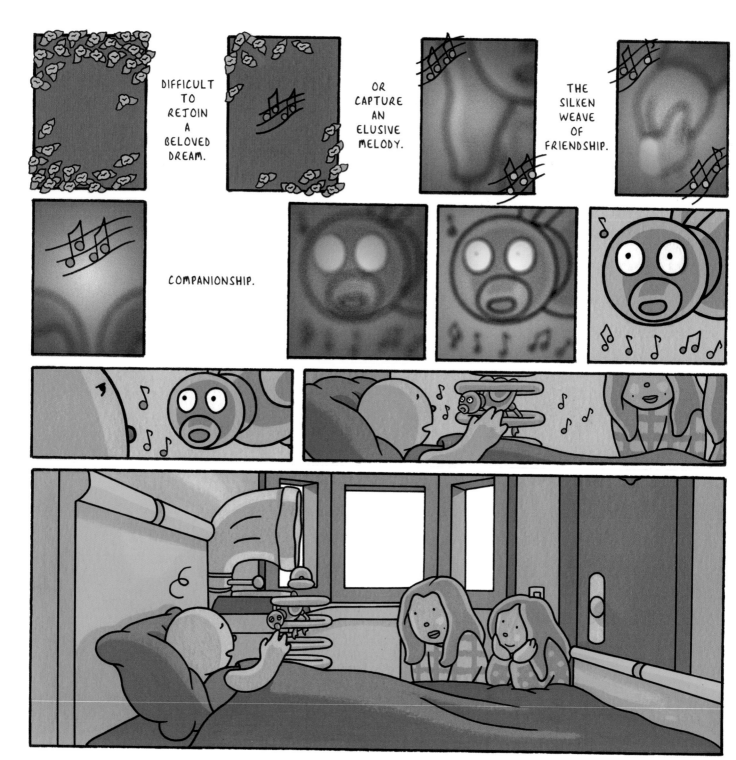

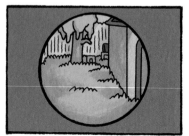

OF COURSE LOUIS HAD GROWN VEGETABLES AND FRUIT BEFORE.

BUT THE VISITORS HAD TAUGHT HIM ABOUT SEED PROCEDURE AND GERMINATION.

AND, ANYWAY IT WOULD HAVE SEEMED IMPOLITE TO INTERRUPT.

LOUIS WONDERED IF THE SEEDS HAD JOURNEYED FROM AFAR...

LOUIS WASN'T SURE HOW LONG HE HAD BEEN RECUPERATING, EXACTLY.

TIME HAD SEEMED TO SPIRAL, OR FOLD.

AND TIME HAD SEEN A RETURN TO NORMAL WORKING METHODS.

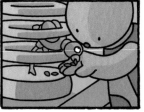

THEY SAY MORT™ IS THE PERFECT FOOD...

BUT PERSONALLY ...

Louis - Night Salad

the trailer

and

Louis - Dreams Never Die

animation:

www.metaphrog.com/louis

* * *

Also by metaphrog:

Louis - Dreams Never Die:

a graphic novel with music by hey and múm + animation, on cd or blue vinyl

Louis - The Clown's Last Words

Louis - Lying to Clive

Louis - Red Letter Day

The First Men on Mercury comic adaptation

of the Edwin Morgan poem: www.metaphrog.com/mercury

Strange Weather Lately

The Maze